CW00926522

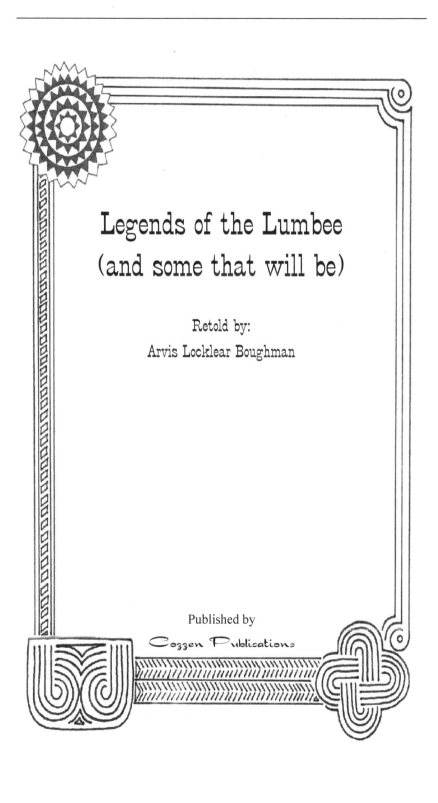

Legends of the Lumbee
(and some that will be)

Retold by:

Arvis Locklear Boughman

Published by

Cozzen Publications

Printed in United States of America
First printing by Cozzen Publications

DEDICATION

In honor and memory of my mother

Adelaide Locklear Boughman

who taught me the meaning of

love, courage, and strength.

Thank you, Mr. Duane Cozzen, Mr. T. A. Fossett, and

Ms. Linda Massengill for all your help!

Table of Contents

A Lumbee Story, shared by
Sharon Locklear, publisher of Metrolina Pow Wow

Author's Note

The Lumbee, people of the dark river swamp, are natural storytellers. Lloyd Lowry, one of the most skilled Lumbee storytellers in the Saddletree Township, would travel around to the local communities spinning his yarns and acting out his haint (ghost), toten (omen), and "booger" stories. More recently, Lumbee storytellers such as Barbara Braveboy Locklear, Gwen Locklear, Barbara Locklear, Mardella Lowry, and Nora Dial-Stanley, carry on this ancient storytelling tradition to a much broader audience.

The Lumbee is the largest Native American tribe east of the Mississippi River. Many Lumbee ancestors were called Cheraw, Keyauwee, Woccon and other related Eastern Siouan tribes. The ancestors of our tribe shared many stories with other local tribes such as the Cherokee, Creek, and Catawba. As our people shared stories, they found that our sister tribes also told tales about mischievous "little wild spirit people", animals, the afterlife, and how our world came to be.

TIMELINE OF SIGNIFICANT EVENTS IN THE HISTORY OF THE LUMBEE INDIANS

DATE(S)	EVENTS
12,000 B.C. - 1700	Spear and arrow point discovered in the Robeson Trails Archaeological survey. Prove Robeson County was occupied by Indians during this period.
1539	Spanish under Hernado DeSoto were among the first Europeans to make contact with the ancestors of many Lumbee called the Cheraw.
1703	Cheraw leave Danville, Virginia for Cheraw, South Carolina.
1703 - 1737	Cheraws are documented as living on the Pee Dee River in South Carolina.
1737	Cheraws sell their land on the Great Pee Dee River in South Carolina.
1738	Robert Locklear listed as Chief of Cheraw(Wall Street Journal)

DATE(S)	EVENTS
1753	Drowning Creek, now called the Lumbee River, is proclaimed a "frontier to the Indian" by North Carolina Governor Rowan.
1771	Cheraw settlement on Drowning Creek documented in the *South Carolina Gazette.*
1835	North Carolina passes law preventing Indians from voting and owning or using firearms
1865-1872	Henry Berry Lowrie war in Robeson County to fight oppression of the Lumbee people.
1865	Begins period of Lumbee migration to the Claxton, Georgia area.
1875	The revised NC constitution restored the right to vote to free persons of color. Many Native Americans in NC were misclassified on census records.
1885	NC General Assembly recognized the Indians of Robeson County as Croatan and established a separate school system for Indians.

DATE(S)	EVENTS
1887	Lumbee people build Croatan Indian Normal School (now The University of North Carolina at Pembroke).
1911	The North Carolina General Assembly changes the name of the tribe to Indians of Robeson County.
1912	The Department of the Interior sent Charles F. Pierce, the Supervisor of Indian Schools, to Robeson County to conduct a study of the tribe. He stated in his report that one would readily class a large majority [of the Lumbee] as being at least three-fourths Indian"
1913	North Carolina legislature changes the tribe's name to Cherokee Indians of Robeson County.
1933	Appearance of John R. Swanton's paper, "Probable Identity of the 'Croatan' Indian," which began a movement for federal recognition as Siouans.

DATE(S)	EVENTS
1935	Felix Cohen's memorandum states that Robeson County Indians with ½ or more Indian blood can organize under the Wheeler-Howard Indian Reorganization Act of 1934.
1940	First performance of Ella Deloria's pageant, "The Life Story of a People," in the Cherokee Indian Normal School (UNCP) gym.
1953	Passage of a North Carolina Law, at the urging of DF Lowry and others, to "Lumbee Indians of North Carolina" taken from the name of the river flowing through Robeson County. This is first tribal name, the Indians of Robeson County, had an opportunity on which to vote.
1956	Passage of the federal Lumbee Act (PL-84-570), naming the Indians living in Robeson County as "Lumbee Indians of North Carolina"
1958	Lumbee routs Ku Klux Klan near Maxton. This event is remembered as the "Battle of Hayes Pond."

DATE(S)	EVENTS
1970	First Lumbee Homecoming held in Pembroke, NC
1971	First Native American owned bank in US-Lumbee Bank opens in Pembroke, NC
1973	Henry Ward Oxendine becomes first Native American to serve in the N.C. House of Representatives
1973	Burning of Old Main (UNCP's first brick building constructed in 1923).
1975	Adolph Dial and David Eliades publish *The Only Land I Know: A History of the Lumbee Indians*
1976	First performance of "Strike at the Wind," an outdoor drama depicting the life of Henry Berry Lowry.
1976	Release of *Proud to Be a Lumbee* Willie's Lowry's musical album.
1980	Lumbees voted into membership of the National Congress of American Indians.

DATE(S)	EVENTS
1987	Lumbee petition U. S. Department of the Interior for federal acknowledgement and entry to tribal rolls is denied due to language in the Lumbee Act of 1956.
1988	Murder of Julian Pierce, Lumbee lawyer/advocate and judgeship candidate.
2001	Lumbee Tribal government sworn in.
2009	Lumbee full federal recognition bill passed the US house and was approved by the US Senate Committee on Indian Affairs.
2010	Jimmy Lowry passes away. Chairman of the North Carolina Commission of Indian Affairs (1977-1984); Wachovia Bank & Trust Advisory Board, High Point, NC; Distinguished Service Award by the Lumbee Regional Development Association; The Order of the Long Leaf Pine, awarded by Governor Jim Hunt in 1981; Member of the US Federal Reserve board.

Rhythm a Little Lumbee

THE ABC'S OF LUMBEE INDIAN LIFE

In honor and memory of Mr. Lewis Barton

A - is for Amazing Grace sang sweetly in church.

Tradition states that some of first churches among the Lumbee were named Old Dogwood, Reedy Branch, Burnt Swamp, Old Prospect, New Jerusalem, Saint Anna, Thessalonica, Union Chapel, and New Hope.

B - is for Baskets, made by Mr. Cleveland and Ms. Loretta, out of oak, pine needles, and birch.

Ms. Loretta Oxendine carries forth the Lumbee tradition of making baskets out of longleaf pine needles bound together with tobacco twine. Mr. Cleveland Jacobs rediscovered his love for basket-making after he had lost his sight. Blind Cleve, as he was affectionately known, wove baskets out of coiled wire grass and white oak or birch splints.

C - is for Corn. Big Red, Indian, and yellow corn picked by me and my cousin.

One of the main items the ancestors of the Lumbee grew and traded was a unique variety of corn or "ku's" called "Big Red" because of the deep red ears which grew on a very tall stalk.

D - is for Dinner on the Ground with ants crawlin' and flies buzzin'.

A standing joke in many Lumbee small, country churches goes, *"There are two things we know how to do around here, worship and eat!"* Put the two together and you've got the Lumbee tradition of all-day singing and dinner on the ground.

E - is for Eagle, flying so free and so high.

The Bald and the Golden are the members of the Eagle family found in North America. The eagle is a highly revered bird among the Lumbee and other Native American tribes. In fact, when a Lumbee individual is honored, he/she is often given an eagle feather in recognition of the deed or accomplishment.

F - is for Fishing in the Lumbee River while eating Aunt Hazel's sweet peach pie.

Fishing is a favorite Lumbee past time. In the past, many Lumbee families would take two week long fishing vacations to the ocean. Families also enjoyed catching "redbreast" bream in the local swamp or Lumbee river. Before going fishing, elders would often throw grass in the air to determine if the wind was favorable for catching fish.

G - is for Gourds, used as swimming floats, or hung on a tall pole to attract the flying Purple Martin.

The Purple Martin is a member of the swallow family. They are a popular bird with the Lumbee because they eat large of amounts of harmful mosquitoes.

H - is for Henry Berry Lowrie, the hero of the Lumbee people; just ask Mr. Bruce Barton.

THE HERO OF A PEOPLE by Adolph L. Dial

Henry Berry Lowrie where are you? Sleeping in an unknown grave? Does the grass grow above your breast, or do dark waters flow? With secret sounds through your bones that will confuse mankind until the end of time, from everlasting to everlasting, you are the hero of a people. Keep your secrets as you sleep—That is part of your greatness.

I - is for Indian. Lumbee Indian Young'uns, playing hide and go seek with skinned up knees.

Lumbee "young'uns," like all children, enjoy playing games out-doors such as tag and jump rope. Baseball is a popular organized sport among Lumbee youth.

J - is for Jam. Tangy and sweet Huckleberry Jam, smeared on bread, eaten under a grove of Persimmon trees.

Huckleberry is also called blueberry. The Persimmon was called "edre" or "possum fruit tree" in the ancient tongue of many Lumbee ancestors. Many Lumbee enjoy Persimmon or Huckleberry fruit raw or cooked in pies, jams, jellies, or puddings.

K - is for Kissing Cousins. Chase me around the tobacco barn! Catch me if you can!

North Carolina without tobacco barns would be like Holland without windmills. The traditional tobacco barn has long been symbol of the traditional farm in Tar Heel life. In the modern age, abandoned tobacco barns are rapidly disappearing.

L - is for Lumbee Homecoming. Lumbee folks coming back home from far and near to Indian Land.

Lumbee Homecoming is held every year around the fourth of July. Homecoming is a time for Lumbee people to gather together to celebrate family, friends, and Native American culture.

M - is for Market. Going to town to sell the vegetables the family picked fresh and sealed in a jar.

Farming was the main livelihood of most Lumbee families in the 19th and 20th centuries. These farmers raised many crops in the rich black and sandy soil of Robeson County including cucumbers, peanuts, corn, soybeans, watermelon, collards, and cantaloupe. Going to town to sell vegetables was often a family social event.

N - is for Nature. Listen to the birds, crickets, and frogs singing in a wild choir.

Many varieties of animals live in the woodlands and swamps of Lumbee land including black bear, opossum, deer, ducks, geese, rabbits, raccoons, and snakes.

O - is for Old Main at UNCP. The Lumbee people almost lost that beloved building in a fire.

Willie French Lowry, Lumbee Indian musician sang, "It's just a building but it means so much, to the Lumbee people. It stood alone when no others were around. People cried, on the night, they tried to burn Old Main down. Come on people, let's save Old Main."

P - is for Powwow dancers whirling, twirling, and prancing in the sand.

A Powwow is a way that many Native American tribes meet together to join in dancing, visiting, renewing old friendships, and making new ones. The Lumbee hold a spring and fall powwow each year.

Q - is for Quilt. Cloth scraps sewn together in a star/pinecone design, lovingly, by hand.

Vernon Cooper, Lumbee wisdomkeeper, revered elder herbal remedy and lore specialist stated that one his earliest memories involved helping his mother cut strips of cloth (triangles) to make a design in each quilt. His mother called each design a star.

R - is for the Old Railroad Depot in Pembroke. The memory of that place will forever stand.

The first railroad came to Robeson county in 1860, about a year before the civil war. It was called the Wilmington, Charlotte and Rutherfordton Railroad Company (WC&R). When the depot was built in the late 1800's, it became the center of the attention in Pembroke Its existence benefited the areas agricultural trade and became a "window on the world" for many Lumbee people.

S - is for Swimming in Big Raft Swamp, dripping wet, red eyed, and pecan tanned.

Swimming is a great way to cool off on a hot summer's day, but it is also very dangerous activity in the dark waters of Drowning Creek (Lumbee River).

T - is for Tea. Iced Tea tasting so sweet and good after working all day in a hot field.

Drinking sweetened iced tea is a popular southern and Lumbee tradition. Many southern foods and drinks began as Native American traditional cuisine (i.e., grits, hominy, fried squash).

U - **is for Unity. It's something not given away for free. It's something that is important to build.**

Webster's Dictionary defines Unity as "a condition of harmony or the quality or state of being made one."

V - **is for Victory at Hayes Pond over the Klan.**

The Ku Klux Klan burned crosses in the yard of two Lumbee Indian families in 1958. Afterwards, hundreds of Lumbee gathered at a Klan rally near Maxton, NC. They broke up a Klan rally and chased the members out of Robeson County. The Klan did not return for over 20 years.

W - **is for Whistling Rufus, Prospect community's very own music man.**

Any man, woman, or child, who lives in a Lumbee community, has probably earned a nickname. John R. Lowry's nickname was Whistling Rufus. Mr. John or "Rufus" was known for whistling a happy tune while he walked up and down the roads of the Prospect community.

X - **is for Xuala (Shoewala), which is what DeSoto called some of the Lumbee ancestors peeking at the Spaniards from behind a vine.**

In 1540 Hernando DeSoto led a large group of conquistadors through what is now the southeastern United States from Florida to southwestern North Carolina. One native tribe DeSoto met was a group they called Joara or Xuala. This tribe was later called the Cheraw. Many Lumbee are descendants of the Cheraw tribe.

Y - **is for Yellow or Longleaf Pine from which we made the naval stores of Tar, Pitch, and Turpentine.**

Products from pine resin were called naval stores because ship-builders would use tar and pitch to water proof ship's wooden hulls and protect ropes and ladders in the 17th, 18th, and 19th centuries.

Z - **is for Zinna. My great grandma rocking my grandpa Loy to sleep when he was a baby. She would whisper, "Sssh! Please stop cryin'!"** ZZzzzzzz! Good Night!

Many Lumbee ancestors were known in the past as the "keepers of the turtle mound." The great turtle mound was known as a gathering place for trade, ceremonies, and fellowship for many of the southeastern US tribes. The Lumbee tribe views the Lumbee River as the cultural and spiritual center of their community. There are many summers in the land of the Lumbee, where drought is coupled with extremely high temperatures. Historians state that the area that is now Robeson County was once 70-80% swampland. To be able to use this land for farming, drainage ditches or ditchbanks were dug to drain the swamp water from many areas. This ancient tale attempts to explain how the Lumbee and other rivers were formed.

Rabbit Steals Water
from the Snapping Turtle

In the long ago, the animals were much bigger than they are now. The mother of Snapping Turtles was bigger than the Lumbee River. She sat on top of the great mother spring and kept most of the water of the world from flowing out. The Snapping Turtle always seemed to be in an ill mood and would never speak to any of the other animals, except to grunt "Umph!"

One summer's day, it was so hot that the morning dew did not collect on the plants. Rabbit would usually lick the dew off the plants before sunrise. He whined, "There is not one cloud in the sky, and I am so hot and my mouth is so dry. I think I will hop over to the creek to find some water."

When Rabbit arrived at the creek, he found that it had dried up. Even the bottom of the creek bed was dry and dusty. Rabbit thought, "Beaver will know where I can find some water."

So Rabbit followed the dry creek gully down to Beaver's lodge. When Rabbit found Beaver's home, Rabbit grabbed one of the sticks and began beating on Beaver's home yelling, "Beaver! Are you here?" Just then, Rabbit heard a long wail. Rabbit followed the sound up another dry canal where he found Beaver crying, "Mi, mi, mi mi,.."

Rabbit asked, "What happened to the creek?"

Beaver moaned, "I don't know. One night I was swimming around my lodge and the next morning the water was gone."

Rabbit whined, "Do you know someone who could tell us what's happened?"

Beaver sobbed, "I don't know, but Muskrat, who lives upstream from here, might know what to do."

Rabbit asked, "Do you want to come with me?" Beaver cried, "No I think I will just sit here and cry, but please let me know if you find anything ow-ow-ow out."

Rabbit traveled up the dry creek bed for a long way and found Muskrat lying under a huge sycamore tree. Muskrat was snoring loudly with all four feet sticking up in the air. Rabbit poked Muskrat in the ribs.

Muskrat mumbled, "Who issss kicking me?"

Rabbit grumbled, "Wake up, Do you know what happened to the water?"

Muskrat yawned, "It'sss that old Sssssnapping Turtle. The ssssprings and the ssssstreams have all shrunk sssso sssssmall becaussse of thisss sssweltering sssummer and that ssselfish whipper sssnapper turtle."

Rabbit asked, "Do you want to go with me to visit the turtle?" Muskrat rolled over and murmured, "I'm sssad theress's no ssstreams and ssssprings, but I am ssso sssleepy. If you ssstumble across sssome news, come whisssper it in my earsss."

Rabbit traveled for almost half a day. He was panting and about to faint from the heat when he finally arrived at the great mother spring. Rabbit crawled up to the huge turtle and begged, "Kind mother of all snapping turtles, let me have some water because I am so hot and thirsty."

The Snapping Turtle grunted, "Umph!" and turned her massive head away. Rabbit pleaded, "If you will let just a trickle of water go, my friends and I will be most thankful."

The Snapping Turtle bellowed, "Umph, NO!"

While the Snapping Turtle was looking away, Rabbit had dug a small ditch in the ground under the great turtle so the water could run out.

So much water ran out, it made gullies. These gullies made streams, and the streams came together to form the Lumbee and other rivers. The rivers formed big pools which we call oceans and seas. Beaver stopped his crying because his creek filled up, and Muskrat finally woke up when he heard the water come rushing back. Ever since Rabbit dug the first ditchbank under the Snapping Turtle, the water has flowed very well.

Tobacco has earned a bad reputation in our society, but the Lumbee have grown tobacco for centuries. In the old time, tobacco was not used in extreme amounts but was utilized in special ceremonies to greet, honor, present as a gift, give thanks, and cure illnesses. The Lumbee also used tobacco seeds in a poultice to treat boils and or treat stomach discomforts and other ailments. This Eastern Siouan tale explains why the Hummingbird was viewed by many ancestors of the Lumbee as a messenger of God.

HOW THE HUMMINGBIRD BROUGHT BACK THE TOBACCO

In the old time, when people and animals saw each other as brothers and sisters, there was only one tobacco plant.

The four-footed (animals) and two-footed (birds and people) nations would travel a long way just to take a small piece of the leaf. However, Eha'sure' the Goose, became greedy and wanted the tobacco all to herself. She snatched the plant out of the ground and carried it far away to the south. The people and animals began suffering without their tobacco medicine. One wise Raccoon grew very sick, and the medicine keeper said she would die unless she received the tobacco medicine.

Many animals and people tried to steal the tobacco plant away from the Goose. The larger ones tried first and then the smaller ones. But, Ehasure' the Goose would peck and beat anyone coming near the plant.

Meanwhile, the old Raccoon grew sicker every day.

After all the other animals and people had tried, the little Mole attempted to reach the plant by digging to it underground, but Goose's friend Wis pak pak the Robin tilted her head to the side and heard the little mole digging under the ground. Goose and Robin dug him out, beat and pecked him, and sent the Mole home bruised and sore.

Hummingbird had offered to go before, but the two-footeds and four-footeds thought the little bird was too small to help.

Finally, after begging them for a long time, the people and animals showed the Hummingbird a plant in the middle of a field near the Red Spring The animals said to him, "Use that plant to show us how you would get the tobacco." In the next instant, Hummingbird was gone, and all the people and animals saw the small bird sitting on top of the plant. Before the animals could blink again, the Hummingbird was back. No one had seen him going or coming because he was so swift. "That's exactly how I will get the tobacco," said the Hummingbird. The animals decided to let him try.

Hummingbird started on his journey and after he had flown about a half a day, he found the tobacco, with Ehasure' the Goose and Wis pak pak the Robin standing guard on opposite sides of the plant. The little bird darted down to the plant. Apo! Robin and Goose could not see the Hummingbird because he was so small and flew so fast. Hummingbird snatched the top of the plant with the tiny sucker leaves and seeds and was off again before the Goose and Robin knew what had happened. Before the Hummingbird arrived home, the Raccoon fell down sick and the people and animals thought she was near death. However when Hummingbird returned, they carried Raccoon to a circular grove of trees. The people and the animals took some tobacco leaves, sweet grass, and mint, burned them together, and smudged/smeared some of the tree trunks with the ashes. Then they took some of the remaining leaves and made a tea. They used the remaining seeds to grow new plants. After Raccoon drank the tea, she opened her eyes, cried "Ipa (tobacco)!" and was well again.

Most Lumbee Indians descend from a group of closely related tribes called the Eastern Siouan or Piedmont Tribes. Tribes such as the Catawba, Keyauwee, Waccamaw, and Cheraw were major Eastern Siouan groups. The Cheraw and Keyauwee once called the Northwestern highlands of North Carolina, now called the Sauratown mountains, their home. In later years, they also called the Central highlands of North Carolina, now called the Uwharrie mountains, home. This tale is taken from an old Eastern Siouan story about how the unique colors of the Rhododenron /Laurel and other plants came to be.

THE LEGEND OF THE LAUREL

When the world was young, Waro'we (God/Never Die) gave the lesser spirits tasks to perform. The spirit of the East Wind was given the task of painting the morning sky at sunrise with blue, gray, and yellow-orange. The spirit of the West Wind was given the task of painting the evening sky with peachy pink, pearly purple, ochre orange, and ruby red.

One evening, the West Wind was flying above the earth carrying the paint for the evening sunset. As he was soaring above the Sauratown mountains, the West Wind looked down on the earth and saw a beautiful Indian maiden picking wild blueberries on the slope of Jomeokee, the guiding mountain. West Wind was so taken with the maiden's beauty that he forgot all about the paint that he was carrying, and he spilled his orange paint on the flame azaleas and Oak trees of the Sauratown mountains. As he flew, he also spilled his ruby red on the maple trees, his pearly purples on the wild plum trees, and his peachy pinks on the laurel bushes of the Uwharrie mountains.

To this day it is said that if one travels to the former home of many Lumbee, in the Uwharrie and Sauratown highlands, he may see orange flame azaleas, the peachy-pink laurel thickets, and the pearly-purple colored wild plum trees.

Native Americans of North and Central America introduced corn, beans, tobacco, tomatoes, chocolate, and squash to the entire world. Many social activities such as dances, spiritual gatherings, powwows, hog killings, and corn shuckings still occur around harvest time in many Lumbee Indian communities. Several southeastern tribes also have a similar tale to The Race at White Hill involving a race between the deer and turtle.

THE RACE AT WHITE HILL

W hen the world was young, Wideboye' the Deer, loved to brag about being a mighty runner. All the animal nation knew that Kaya, the Turtle was a great warrior, but as quickness went, they only thought of him as a slow traveler. One day Deer was bragging as usual, and Kaya grew tired of all the boasting. The Turtle began fussing with Deer shouting, "You may be the fastest talker in the animal nation, but I am the quickest runner." Deer and Turtle argued day and night for three days. Deer would exclaim, "I can run from Red Bank to Big Bay in less than half a day!" "That's snail's travel," grumbled the Turtle, "I can cover that distance in half that time."

The animals had heard this talk for three days and had grown tired of the all the yelling back and forth. The nations decided to arrange a race between the two to settle the quarrel once and for all. Deer wanted to start at sun up and race until the moon rose, but Bear explained, "A long distance race could not be judged. A much shorter distance would work out much better."

All the animals agreed that the race should begin at sunrise on the first day of the next new moon at the base of White Hill. The animals named this place White Hill because of the pure white sand found on its small slope. It was also agreed that Turtle and Deer would race across four great fields. Tall stalks of "Big Red" Corn grew in the first field. The second field grew thick bushy bean vines. Broad yellow leaf tobacco grew in the third field, and golden squash grew in the fourth field. Between each field was a great wide ditch. The first animal to cross these four fields and the ditches in between would be the winner. The animals shouted, "The plan is good and fair."

Deer felt so confident that he snorted, "You don't know how to run, and you'll never win the race. I'm so sure that I will win this race that I'll give you a head start across the first field." Kaya replied, "I'll take your offer, but I don't really need it."

Later that evening the turtle clan came for a council meeting beside the Lumbee river. When all of his turtle children, his turtle wife, his turtle aunts, his turtle cousins were gathered together, Kaya the Turtle sighed, "I know I should not have told Deer that I was faster, because it's not true. I grew tired of Deer's bragging, and I spoke without thinking. I do have a plan to win but I need everyone's help."

When the day of the race came, all the animals gathered around the base of White Hill at dawn. Deer was strutting about and boasting as usual. The Turtle spoke to no one and began his crawl across the first field. The animals had to wait until the sun was high in the sky before the Turtle finished crawling across the first field of red corn. The deer laughed and snickered the whole time making jokes about how long it took Turtle to crawl across just one field.

Finally, when Turtle had reached the end of the first field, Burnt Swamp Bear, who was standing on a stump on the top of White Hill, raised his paw high in air as a signal that the race was ready to begin. Then the bear dropped his great black furry paw to his side shouting, "Dane!'" or go, the signal for the Deer to start. Zip! Deer began with long leaps bounding across the cornfield. He thought, "I will win the race before Turtle can crawl out of the first ditch." When Deer leapt out of the cornfield and across the gully, Deer saw that Turtle was far ahead of him crawling into the second ditch.

Deer had no doubt that he would catch-up to the Turtle in the second field of bushy beans. As Deer ran out of the second field, he stopped in his tracks and rubbed his eyes in disbelief when he saw Turtle scratching out of the second ditch crawling into the third field which grew the broad-leaf yellow tobacco.

Deer snorted with worry because he could not understand how Turtle had gotten so far ahead of him. So, he made several great leaps to try to catch Turtle. After Deer leapt out of the third field that grew the tobacco, Deer's eyes became as wide as gourds as he watched the pokey Turtle crawl into the fourth and last field of golden squash. Deer was wet with sweat and he knew the finish line was at the end of the squash field, so he gathered himself and ran through the squash field faster than the wind. As Deer came in sight of the finish line he wheezed, "I did it. I am going to win," But, at that moment Deer's heart sank because he saw Turtle crawling across the finish line to win the race. As Turtle crossed over the line all the animals shouted, "Kaya is the fastest runner in the animal nation." Deer could not make another jump to finish the race, instead, he fell over in the tall grass at the edge of the golden squash field panting, just as Deer do today when they feel tired, thirsty, or humble.

Of course all the animals agreed that Kaya the Turtle had won the race, but they wondered how he could win against such a swift runner as Deer. Turtle never told them, but around the fire at the Turtle clan's stomp dance that night, Kaya the Turtle and his family laughed about how easy it had been to fool Wideboye' the Deer. Every member of the Turtle clan looked just alike. Kaya's cousin was the one who began the race. Kaya had posted one of his family at the end of each field and in every ditch in between the fields before dawn. And, whenever Deer came into sight, one cousin would crawl out of the ditch and hide in the next field. When Turtle himself saw Deer jumping out of the last field of squash, he left his hiding place in the tall grass to cross the finish line. That is how Kaya the Turtle bested the Deer in the great race at White Hill, the elders say. It has been rumored around the Animal Nation that Turtle cheated. But it is true that Deer has boasted very little since.

This tale was told by Earl Carter, the Lumbee Keeper of the Sacred Fire. In the old time, the holy man or keeper would tend to the sacred flame of the people, making sure it was kept burning all year. With each new cycle/year, he would start a new holy "sacred fire" from the burning coals of the previous year's fire. This keeper was also the expert on healing and herbal remedies for the tribe. In modern times, the keeper leads spiritual gatherings and prays for the sick. He also guides healings, treatments with sacred herbs to heal and keep away evil, shares the tales/culture of the tribe, cleanses the sacred dancing circle, and directs naming ceremonies for babies. This tale shares how Black Widow sought to steal and keep the most "sacred fire" of all, the sun.

HOW THE BLACK WIDOW

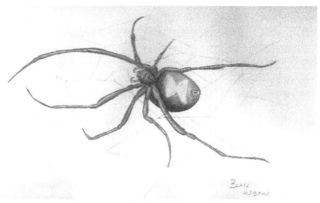

STOLE THE SUN

In the old time, before people walked the earth, Black Widow, the spider, made her home in a wide, deep, dark hole in the earth. Widow, as she was called by the other animals, lived deep underground so that she would not have to talk or dance with anyone. However, one thing she did miss was the warmth and light of the sun. It was very dark, damp, and cold where she lived. One day Widow decided she would spin a great web. She spun her web so high and so strong that she was able to reach the sun. But as Widow was covering the sun in her web, the sun's heat was so hot that it burnt widow black. Even though she was badly burned, she tightly wrapped the sun in her spider web, and carefully climbed back down into her hole, dragging the sun with her into to her lair.

The earth became cold and dark without the sun. The two-leggeds and four-leggeds stumbled as they felt their way through the forest to the gathering place, the Council Oak. The no-leggeds, the snakes, also joined the gathering. When everyone arrived, the two-leggeds, the birds, told how they saw Widow drag the sun into her lair deep inside the earth. The Animal Nation council agreed that the sun must be returned to its rightful place in the sky. However, no one volunteered to bring the sun back. Racer, the quickest of all snakes, finally agreed to try.

The great snake grandfather of all Racers slithered around in the darkness until he saw a dim light coming from a gaping hole in the ground. As he slid down the hole, the air became warm and he found he could see more clearly the further he crawled down. When Racer arrived at the bottom of the hole, he saw the sun glowing brightly. But he did not see Widow anywhere.

Widow had taken her spider web covering off of the sun. Racer inched closer and decided he would coil himself around the sun and try to pull it out quickly. Racer thought his thick scales would protect him from the heat. The snake pulled and towed the great ball about half way out of the hole, but Racer was a long thin snake and could not bear the great weight of the sun. He had no choice but to let the sun fall back into the hole. It landed with a thud that echoed long and low underground. Racer was burnt jet black from wrapping himself around the sun. To this day the Racer is as inky black as a moonless night.

The Animal Nation council met again at the Council Oak. By now, the earth was turning to ice and was bitterly cold. The animal council once again asked who would go to bring back the sun. No one volunteered to go. Possum and Pocosin Moccasin finally agreed. Possum and Moccasin were old friends who lived deep in the swamp. They were the huge grandparents of the Possum and Water Moccasins we see today. Possum had a bit of silky gray fur at the tip end of her tail. Moccasin was a brown powerful snake with two fangs: long, red, and sharp.

Before Possum and Moccasin went down into the hole they came up with a plan. Firefly helped them find the hole in the darkness. As the friends climbed deeper into Widow's lair, they could see a faint light. Widow had wrapped the sun up in her web again, and the pair could see the great spider sleeping beside the glowing ball. Moccasin slid down to the bottom of the hole and bit into the spider's webbing.

Possum and Moccasin locked tails and began towing the sun out of the hole. Widow's web slipped off part of the sun and the fiery ball landed with a thud, waking Widow.

After the sun fell, Possum immediately wrapped her tail around the sun and began pulling with all her might, but Widow sunk her spider fangs into the sun and began pulling with all of her might. They pulled back and forth for a long while until a piece of the sun broke off in Widow's fangs. The fiery sphere was catapulted out of the hole and back up into the sky.

The old ones say that what was left of Possum's tail fur was scorched off. And, as the heat passed in front of Possum, Possum's face hair became white and her eyes began to glow pink. The Pocosin Water Moccasin is sometimes called the "Cottonmouth" because his mouth was burnt white when he bit into the web covering the sun, but some of the white spider-webbing remained. Because of what happened to his mouth, Water Moccasin is ill-tempered and is friends with no one to this day. When the sun was soaring back up into the sky, it hit Raven and her feathers were seared black. However, Black Widow was able to hold on to and keep a little piece of the sun, which she and her children keep on their bellies to this day.

The Lumbee Indians and other people of the rural Southeast have created a special name for the rich pine they used to start fires. They called these pine splinters or stump wood, lightered (lie-terd). In fact, the first newspaper printed for the University of North Carolina at Pembroke was called The Lightered Knot. UNCP was originally opened in the late 1800's as Indian Normal School. This school was founded to train Lumbee men and women to teach the children of the tribe. In this tale, the Rabbit lives up to his traditional role as the trickster.

HOW THE RABBIT STOLE FIRE FROM THE BUZZARDS

When only animals and plants lived on the earth, the Turkey Buzzards were the keepers of the fire. These giant great grandparents of today's buzzards would not share anything with any of the other animals. They were the stingiest members of the two-legged nation.

On one cold night, Paksa' the Rabbit was trying to sleep in his burrow, a hole in the ground in the middle of a briar thicket, when the icy Northwest Wind found Rabbit and decided to play a trick on him. The Northwest Wind pursed his lips and blew his cold breath down the Rabbit's hole.

When the frigid breath hit Rabbit, the long eared bunny sat up and squealed, "Brrr! I am frosty." The Rabbit shook himself, peeped out of his hole, and spotted something shimmering through the drooping trees of the forest.

The Rabbit went to see what could be glowing in the night. Ahead in a clearing, Rabbit found the Turkey Buzzards sitting around a fire in a tight circle, holding their beaks high in the air. Their large wings were spread so far apart that only faint rays of orange firelight could be seen between the giant birds.

The Rabbit was so very cold that he decided to ask the buzzards if he could warm himself by the fire. Rabbit whined, "Please, kind buzzards, let me get close to the fire. I am so very cold. Isune', the chief buzzard, sneered, "No, we own the fire!"

Rabbit went away acting sad; his ears flopped down on each side of his head. He hopped slowly until he came to an old hollow tree which was Possum's home. Rabbit rapped on the hollow tree, tap, **tap, tap!** Possum hissed, "Whoizit?" Rabbit whispered, "It's me, your old friend Rabbit. Move over and let me sleep here with you." Possum moved over, but Possum's hollow tree was too small for both Possum and Rabbit. Rabbit had to sleep hunched over with his white tail sticking out of the hollow tree.

The cold Northwest Wind found Rabbit asleep again and had to giggle when he saw Rabbit's white cotton tail sticking out of the old tree. The Northwest Wind could not resist pinching the little white tail with his long bony fingers.

Rabbit hopped up and hit his head on the entrance to Possum's lodge and howled, "Ow, wheee! Who is pinching me? What a dirty trick!" Rabbit looked to the left and to the right, but he could not see the Northwest Wind snickering behind a big Poplar tree. Then Rabbit thought to himself, "My front is warm, but my whole backside, especially my little white tail, is about to freeze off." Rabbit decided to go see the buzzards a second time.

"Please, O' please!" the Rabbit pleaded, "Let me just stick my little tail near the fire. It feels like it's going to freeze off." Isune' the chief buzzard lifted his huge beak higher in the air and yawned, "No, no, you can't do that. We own the fire."

Rabbit went away again with his head hung low. Finally he lay down under a big pine tree and covered himself with pine needles. However, Rabbit's long feet were poking out of the pile of needles. The Northwest Wind still wanted to play, so he waited until Rabbit fell asleep and wiggled and jiggled his icy blue fingers tickling Rabbit's feet. Rabbit started laughing, "He, he, he! Ho, ho, ho! Mi, mi mi!"

Rabbit sprang up to see who was tickling his feet, but there was no one to be seen. He did not see the Northwest Wind silently belly laughing, sitting on a longleaf pine branch above Rabbit's head. Rabbit thought to himself, "Someone is still playing tricks on me, and my poor little toes feel like they could freeze together."

Just then, Rabbit saw an old pine stump sticking out of the ground beside where he lay. Rabbit came up with an idea.

Rabbit visited the Turkey Buzzards a third time and cried, "Please O' please! "Just let me stick my toes near the fire." Isune', the chief Buzzard, tilted his beak toward the sky and bellowed, "No, no, no, you can't do that. We own the fire!" Rabbit started to cry and moan. One buzzard, sitting around fire, felt sorry for Rabbit and lifted up his wing so that Rabbit could put his toes close to the fire.

No one knew that Rabbit had placed pine splinters between his toes. Humming a tune, the Rabbit crept underneath the kind buzzard's wing and put his foot near the fire. A few sparks jumped out of the flame and lighted the pine splinters. Rabbit hummed, "Oh, my foot is getting warmer. It's getting warmer. Wonaire', thank you! Oh, oh, oh! My foot is hot. It's so hot!"

Rabbit ran off because the sparks had turned into fire, and the flame was burning Rabbit's feet. Rabbit zipped through the woods, jumping, howling, and singing this song to ease his pain. "Ow, Rabbit is wise. Ow, Rabbit is pretty. Ow whee! Rabbit is smart! Oh, ow, ow, oh the fire will be so big! The whole Animal Nation can come, sit down, and warm themselves by the fire."

Rabbit raced back to his home in the briar thicket and there he shook the splinters out of his toes into the thorns. The flames shot up immediately making a huge fire. The entire Animal Nation saw the fire and gathered around it on that cold winter's night. To this day, the fur inside the rabbit's toes is white where it had burned long ago. The old ones say that this is how Rabbit stole fire from the buzzards.

In many Native American tales, the Possum and Rabbit are usually portrayed as tricksters. Animal tales hold a special place in many southeastern tribes' lore. The Possum, and other animals, were often given human characteristics to help people relate to the char-acters and learn valuable lessons about life.

HOW THE POSSUM TRICKED
THE DEER, BEAR, AND WOLVES

many ancestors of the Lumbee called Possum Dupatustre', or "one with tail of no hair". But at the beginning of the world, Possum was proud of his bushy tail with its silky gray fur.

One cold winter's day, the Possum went out in the snow and found a Persimmon tree, now called the "Possum fruit tree," growing in the Winnabow Woods. The Possum sang to himself, "Here I am by myself, with my beautiful tail, and I have found some persimmons to eat." So, he ate all the persimmons he could find laying on the ground.

The Possum was so lazy that he usually slept till late evening and would do anything to get out of working for a meal. Possum was still hungry after eating all the persimmons he could find on the ground, and was feeling too lazy to climb up in the tree.

Just then, the Deer came along and asked, "What are you doing here?" The Possum replied, "Eating persimmons." The Deer looked on the ground and then up into the tree and asked, "How did you get them out of the tree?" The Possum hissed and lied through his teeth, "I wanted the persimmons so I walked back from the tree, ran as hard as I could, and butted the tree with my head until the persimmons began to fall like rain." It was very hard to find food in the winter so the Deer walked back from the tree, stamped, pawed the ground, ran as fast as he could, and butted the tree with his head. The persimmons did fall like rain, but Deer felt too dizzy from hitting the tree, and didn't eat any of them. He staggered away with a big pumpknot on his head and a bad headache. Meanwhile, Possum quickly gobbled up all the new persimmons.

The Possum was still hungry after eating all these persimmons that had fallen to the ground, and he was still too lazy to climb up the tree. Just then, Bear waddled up the trail and asked, "What are you doing here?" The Possum replied, "Eating persimmons." The Bear looked on the ground and then up into the tree and asked, "How did you get them out of the tree?" The Possum hissed and lied through his teeth, "I wanted the persimmons so I walked back from the tree, ran as hard as I could, and butted the tree with my head again and again until the persimmons began to fall like rain." Bear snarled, "If I butted the tree like that my head would get hurt. How did you really get the persimmons out of the tree?" Possum hissed and lied through his teeth again, "I wanted the persimmons so I climbed the tree and went out on the branch that had the most persimmons and I held on with my front paws and shook it until the persimmons fell like rain." It was very hard to find food in the winter so the Bear went into the woods, found his basket, and returned to the tree. He began to climb the tree until he had found the branch that held the most persimmons. Then Bear climbed out on the branch, then slid down until he was holding on with his front paws. Bear began to shake the limb with all his strength and the persimmons did fall like rain. However, the branch was covered with slippery snow. And after a few great, hard, shakes, Bear lost his grip, fell off the tree limb, and hit the ground with a thud. Then, moaning "Wooo," Bear went limping back to the forest with a bruised rump. Again, Possum quickly ate up all the persimmons Bear had left behind.

The Possum was still hungry after eating all the new persimmons that had fallen to the ground, and once again he was feeling too lazy to climb up the tree. He sang to himself, "Here I am, by myself, with my beautiful tail, and I still want more persimmons to eat."

Just then, the Chief Wolf came along and asked, "What are you doing here?" The Possum replied, "Eating persimmons." The chief wolf looked up and asked, "How did you get them out of the tree?" The Possum hissed and lied through his teeth, "I wanted the persimmons so I walked back from the tree, ran as hard as I could, butted the tree with my head and the persimmons fell like rain." The Chief Wolf snarled, "If I butted the tree with my head, I would get hurt. How did you really get the persimmons out of the tree?" The Possum hissed and lied through his teeth again, "I wanted the persimmons so I climbed the tree and went out on the branch that had the most persimmons and I held on with my front paws and shook it until the persimmons fell like rain." The Chief Wolf walked over to the other side of the tree and sniffed the bear's basket and asked Possum, "Where did you get this?" Before Possum could lie through his teeth again, Wolf growled, "I saw Deer staggering around with a pump knot on his head, and I saw Bear limping around with a bruised rump. You have lied and you know that is against our code. My brothers and I are very hungry, so instead of persimmons I think we will have you for a meal." It was very hard to find food in the winter, so the Chief Wolf barred his teeth and the Wolf's brothers began coming out of the woods on all sides. Possum almost decided to "play possum," or pretend to die of fright, but he thought it better to run up the Persimmon tree to try to get away.

The Possum climbed from the Persimmon tree to another tree, and still another tree, and on and on until the wolves lost sight of him. Finally, the wolves came to the bank of the Lumbee river.

The Chief Wolf said, "Brothers we shall have no meal tonight." As the Chief Wolf was saying these words the wolves heard, "plop, plop, plop." Something was dripping into the river. Chief Wolf looked up and saw Possum on a Longleaf Pine branch, almost directly above his head, laughing with the slobber from his mouth dripping into the river. Possum thought he was out of danger because he was so high up into the tree, but he did not know that wolves are great leapers. The Chief Wolf jumped high into the air and bit the part of the Possum's tail that was hanging down. The Chief Wolf wiggled and twisted as he held tight to the Possum's tail. The Possum also pulled and pulled. Finally, the Wolf twisted around and stripped the

Possum's tail of most of its fur, but the wolf fell into the river with nothing but a mouthful of Possum hair. The Possum felt so embarrassed, for he no longer had a beautiful silky gray fur tail. In fact, Possum's tail had just a little bit of hair left on tip end of it. Possum was so frightened and ashamed that he ran from one tree to another for a great while until he finally hid in an old hollow tree in the middle of a briar thicket.

Ever since the Possum fooled the Deer and Bear he can no longer brag about his furry tail.

If you decide to take a walk one night when the persimmons are ripe, shine your light up in that old persimmon tree. You might just see one of Possum's children up in the branches. If you happen to see one of old Possum's children, ask him, "Have you seen any persimmons?" You might be lucky enough to get hissed at, but don't believe anything the Possum says.

This folktale is an adaptation of an old legend with some rhyming words and place names included for the main characters. Long Swamp, Prospect and Wakulla are places in Robeson County, home of the Lumbee. The Lumbee have known for centuries that pine rosin, boiled in a pot over a fire, or heated at a high temperature would turn into tar. In the late 19th and early 20th centuries, many Lumbee families would travel long distances to places such as Claxton, Georgia so they could collect and market naval stores, products derived from pine rosin such as tar, pitch, and turpentine.

THE LITTLE WOLF AND THE BIG BAD PIG

One day the Wakulla Wolf invited the Prospect Pig to his home, saying, "Please come and visit me on the first night of the next new moon. It's coming up real soon. I'll fix some rich red apples in a thick maple syrup stew, good and tasty just for you." The wild pig agreed to come on the first night of the next new moon to the Wakulla Woods.

On the first night of the new moon, Prospect Pig came to Wakulla woods and squealed, "Wakulla Wolf, where are you? I couldn't have gotten here faster even if I could have flew. My mouth is watering for your rich red apples in maple syrup stew." Suddenly, the wolf jumped out of the bushes and yelled, "Aooo! Surprise, you old boar! I thought you knew, there are no apples ripe in this season to put into a stew. From your long journey, please do take a short rest, but don't stay too long or I might think that you are a pest." After the wolf left, the pig got up and stomped away hot with anger. The wild pig was so mad he began to think of an evil plan to pay the wolf back for his dirty trick.

The next time Prospect Pig saw the Wakulla Wolf, the pig hid his anger and cooed, "Come visit me in Long Swamp on the first night of the next full moon. It's coming up real soon. Where I live the rabbits are thick. So thick, I have to beat them out of my garden with a stick. But, I will catch two for you and two for me and let you have your pick." The wolf licked his lips and agreed to visit the wild pig on the first night of the next full moon.

After the Prospect Pig left the wolf, the pig found four old rabbit skins and scraped the bark and outer pulp of several longleaf pine trees with his hoof until pine rosin ran out of the trees into his bowl. Then the pig let this pine rosin sit in the hot sun until it became thick and gooey tar. The Prospect Pig filled the old rabbit skins with the gooey tar and pine needles and stuck a stick through the tar filled pelts, put them over some logs, and waited for the time of the wolf's visit.

On the first night of the next full moon, Wakulla Wolf came to visit the pig. The wolf strolled up to the wild pig's lodge. The wolf spied, in the moonlight, four rabbits cooking over some hot coals. The wolf thought to himself, "I have come a long way through the swamps and thickets and tripped over more than one tree limb. I'm sure that old boar won't mind if I eat without him." The wolf grabbed one of the rabbit skins and took a big bite. The wolf thought the rabbit was awfully chewy, and when he opened his mouth to take another bite, the Wakulla Wolf realized that his mouth was sealed shut.

The wolf had found out too late that the pig had tricked him by putting tar inside the rabbit skins. The wolf rolled around on the ground and went to the brook to try and wash the tar out of his mouth with water, but nothing could unglue his mouth. The wild pig was hiding and watching from the bushes with his hoof over his mouth trying not to laugh out loud.

The poor wolf was not able to eat for an entire week, and the hungrier he became, the madder he became. When the wolf was able to spread his lips and teeth apart, Wakulla Wolf ran to Prospect Pig's home and growled, "Aoooo, I came here a week ago hungry for rabbit stew. I am so mad and hungry that now I shall have the great pleasure of eating you!" The wild pig noticed the wolf looked much thinner and said, "My neighbor wolf, you are very hungry and tired, that's my guess. Please be seated, just a while, and I will cook up a big mess. As we speak I am preparing you some rabbit stew. You can have some, and I will eat too. As I eat, I will get bigger, you see. And, you can finish the rest of the rabbit stew and then you can eat me."

The wolf sat down and thought, "Hmmm! Rabbit stew and Barbecue, Yum!" The wolf snarled, "No dirty tricks, pig, because after my tail swishes to and fro' two hundred plus two, the stew better be finished because I will be coming to eat you." Then the pig said, "No dirty tricks, but I do have to go find a few wild onions to put in the stew."

Almost as soon as the pig disappeared, the Prospect Pig came running back crying, "A crowd of people are coming this way. Quick, jump into the pot without delay." The wolf had forgotten in his panic that the pot was full of boiling water. Wakulla Wolf jumped into the pot and the Prospect Pig slammed the lid and stood on top of it. That was the end of the Wakulla Wolf.

Today there are seven state/federally recognized Native American tribes in the state of North Carolina which are the Lumbee, Cherokee, Coharie, Meherrin, Haliwa-Saponi, Sappony Indians, Occaneechi Band of Saponi Indians and the Waccamaw-Siouan. This tale takes place in Saddletree, one of six predominantly Lumbee Indian communities, located near Pembroke, NC. This is also a traditional folktale told by the Waccamaw-Siouan people. Storytelling is an ancient honored tradition among the Lumbee and Waccamaw-Siouan peoples.

THE LEGEND OF LAKE WACCAMAW

My cousin Jamie and I were good at getting into trouble. The tall White Oak tree that spread over my Uncle Cecil's old gray barn waved at us in the breeze every day, inviting us to climb up and hide in its green leafy branches. And my uncle's canoe always seemed to be waiting so patiently for us to take it down to our favorite swimming hole in Big Raft Swamp to paddle around and flip it over to quench the heat of a mid-summer's day. When we finished paddling and swimming, we would fish or take a nap under one of the huge Cypress or Pin Oak trees that line the banks of Big Raft Swamp.

On one particularly hot mid-August day, Jamie, his parents, his sisters, and I had just gotten back to the homeplace after a morning spent gathering some corn. We decided to sit down under the Persimmon tree beside the old corncrib for a cold glass of tea and to bust a ripe sweet watermelon. Coming around the corner of the corncrib, we heard a familiar, "Huloh". It was Mr. Loy. It is a custom for our people to honor our elders by using the person's first name with Mr. or Mrs. as a sign of respect. Mr. Loy was taller than a four year old longleaf pine sapling and almost as thin. Mr. Loy had dark copper skin and thick coarse pepper gray hair. An old straw hat covered most of his face. Mr. Loy always dressed in worn out overalls and wore long johns underneath his clothes, (even in the summer). Being polite, we asked Mr. Loy to share the watermelon and a glass of cold sweet iced tea. He took off his hat, wiped the sweat off his forehead with his sleeve, and nodded his head yes to accept the offer.

After Aunt Jo gave Mr. Loy a tall glass of tea, he said, "Thankyou." Then he took a long drink, smacked his lips, and looked over at us and asked "Why ain't you young'uns a swimmin' on dis' hot day?" Jamie replied, "We were a studyin' about goin' when it got a bit cooler." Mr. Loy glanced over and asked, "Have I ever told you about the biggest swimmin' hole around hyur' and how it came to be?" We thought about it a minute and shook our heads, no.

Then, Mr. Loy began to stare straight ahead like he was looking at something far off and said, "My great grand-father told me this story when I was a boy. We sat up and listened because Mr. Loy was the best story and joke teller in Saddletree. Mr. Loy began.

> *In the old time some of our people lived near a place called 'the mound of flowers.' This hill of green plants and flowers was found in the middle of a dry and dusty plain. On this floral mound lived Princess Wenonah. She was the beautiful daughter of Chief Waccamaw.*

Jamie asked, "Waccamaw? Is that like when you 'walk a mile' and get tared?" "No," said Mr. Loy "Dis is a whole lot different." Mr. Loy started again.

> *The princess' people lived just a little piece down the road from the 'mound of flowers.' She was engaged to be married to Mana', the spirit of the eastwind. Mana' looked after her needs so she would never go hungry or need anything. Every year chiefs from near and far would visit the mound of flowers to receive a dawn rose from the hand of the hand of Princess Wenonah. This rose grew wild on the mound. The rose, given by the Princess, would insure good fortune for their tribe for the upcoming year. One day, conniving Chief Ashbow, from the North, visited the mound. When he saw Princess Wenonah, he fell in love with her and went to ask her father for her hand in marriage. Princess Wenonah's father told him nicely that she was already engaged to Mana', the spirit of the east wind. Now, Chief Ashbow was a proud fella', and Chief Waccamaw's answer made him very angry. Chief Ashbow was so mad that he and some of his men attack-*

ed Princess Wenonah's village, killing the princess' father and many of her friends. As Princess Wenonah ran toward her father's village to try and help her people, she was shot by an arrow. Mana', coming to look for his beloved Princess, found her dying in the forest not far from her father's village. With her dying gasps, Princess Wenonah asked Mana' if the mound of plants and flowers could be changed into a lake, filled with pure water and many fish to nourish what was left of her people. Mana' agreed and granted Princess Wenonah's last wish. Mana' tracked down Chief Ashbow and his men, but Chief Ashbow was able to escape and was never heard from again. It is said that the people who were left from Princess Wenonah's tribe watched as a huge flaming rock fell from the heavens and crashed into the mound of flowers. The great mound shook and sank into the earth leaving a huge pit that was filled at once by waters coming from deep within the earth mother. Youngun's, a few dozen miles to the east from this spot, to this day, you can still find that big swimmin' hole filled with fish that I've been tellin' you 'bout.

After Mr. Loy finished his story he got up, stretched his body into a backward C-shape, raised his long bronze arm, and with a great booming laugh, stuck his right hand into a busted half of the watermelon to get the heart, the sweet middle part, out. Then looking straight at Jamie and me with one gray eyebrow raised, Mr. Loy pointed his thin wet watermelon stained finger straight at me and said, "Bucks, stay out of trouble and don't be talking to anyone called Chief Ashbow. We nodded our heads and said, "Yes sir." Mr. Loy smiled, turned, and with long loping steps, disappeared around the corner of the corncrib whistling his way back towards his home. Listening to Mr. Loy talk about water and fish got me in the mood to go swimming, and it turns out we did go swimming on that hot mid-August day. I can still remember laying under a big Cypress tree on the bank of our favorite swimming hole in Big Raft Swamp thinking, "I sure hope Mana' doesn't decide to come back and turn Big Raft Swamp into some kind of 'mound of flowers.'

Scientists believe a giant meteor crashed into the earth many years ago creating a depression where Lake Waccamaw is today in Southeastern North Carolina. Lake Waccamaw is the largest natural freshwater lake on the east coast between New York and Florida. The Waccamaw-Siouan Indian people, to this day, call themselves, "The People of the Fallen Star."

NANE' VISITS THE SPIRIT WORLD

Many Lumbee ancestors were very spiritual people, believing that everything around them was part of their daily worship. Many of these ancestors believed there were two Great Spirits-one good and the other bad. The great good spirit (God) was the maker of the fruits of the fields and the beasts and other creatures of the wilderness. God (Waro'we) made himself known through pleasant streams, towering trees, bright flowers, the sun by day, and the moon by night. The ancestors of many of the Lumbee thought the winds and birds were the messengers of this unseen God, and the good winds were sent to blow his kindness upon them. In appreciation for these blessings, they were very careful to make the "great good spirit" part of all dances, festivals, and songs.

On the other hand, the great bad spirit caused people to be sick ill-tempered. The people repeated chants (secret words for protection) and carried charms to keep bad spirits away.

The medicine men, who fastened a small blackbird above one of their ears as a sign of their office, would make themselves up to appear to be as horrible and frightening as possible, in the hope of scaring away the evil spirits. Bad winds were also sent to warn the people that God was displeased with them. They would say a prayer that is roughly translated, "Much wind is coming. Scatter the wind and roll it away we pray. Watch over us. Hawo (thank you)!"

William Byrd II (1652-1704) was an avid planter, politician, and statesman. He surveyed the Virginia/North Carolina border which is discussed in his most well known literary work, "The History of the Dividing Line." As Byrd and his colleagues were traveling on one of his expeditions, he asked a great Siouan chief Ned Bearskin for an explanation of their religion.

As a rule, the Siouan peoples would not make a reply to such questions, but one Sunday night that silence was broken. Chief Bearskin explained that his people's faith was a secret religion practiced by all the "Piedmont tribes" who spoke a Siouan language. Bearskin told the men that his people believed there was One Supreme God with lesser good spirits. Waro'we (never die), the one supreme God taught the sun, the moon, and stars where they should move in the sky. He explained further that after death there were only two places to go. The good people were directed to a warm country were spring was everlasting. The other place where the dead may go was a cold, dark, and barren country. This tale is an adaptation of "The White Stone Canoe" printed for the Indian education program of Robeson county in the 1970's. It tells about a man's search in strange lands for his one true love.

In the old time there lived a brave man name Nane' and a beautiful Lumbee maiden called Eya' in a village beside the dark and mysterious Lumbee River.

Nane' and Eya' had waited many years for the time they would be married. They had prepared a beautiful little lodge by the Lumbee River, where they would live and raise their family. But as Eya' was bathing in river the night before their wedding, a great Ulagu' (alligator) came up from the dark water of the drowning creek and Eya was no more.

Nane's great heart was not strong enough to endure the loss of his bride. From the time he found out his beloved was gone, there was no peace for him. He had often heard the elders of the tribe say that somewhere there was a "Land of Spirits", but the wise men could not tell him how to get there. Nane' loved Eya so much that knew he had to go and search for his beloved.

One morning Nane' called Eya's dog, Tasiki. He did not say goodbye to the people of the village. Nane' feared the snakes would overhear him and lay in wait for him on the trail. As he walked through the woods, he thought, "How shall I know what path leads me to the 'Land of Spirits?'" Then he remembered that he had heard the old ones say that south (represented by the color red on the great medicine wheel of life) was where life first began. So, guided by the angled shadows of the pine trees during the day and the twinkling stars at night, Nane' headed south.

As Nane' traveled down the Maraskarin road, he noticed there was less bite in the air early in the morning. Tasiki began to splash playfully in every creek they crossed. The forest Sycamores were putting forth tiny leaves, and he began to see colorful wildflowers along the path..

Nane' had traveled a great distance with very little sleep or food. But, one morning, while they were following the forest trail, he came to a giant Oak, taller than any tree in the forest. Underneath the wide spreading branches, the main trail stopped and split into seven smaller paths heading in different directions. Nane' thought about which path to take for a moment, and decided to see what lay on a small path that headed east. Nane' started down that path, but Tasiki wouldn't follow. Tasiki stayed by the tree, sniffing at its gnarled old roots and pawing at the enormous trunk. Nane' scolded Tasiki, but the dog continued to paw the roots and look toward the top of the tree.

"Could this be the great Council Oak the old ones spoke of?" wondered Nane'. The Council Oak was the oldest tree in the world. It was also the biggest tree in the forest. The two-footeds and four-footeds held their great meetings under the branches of this tree long ago. The elders said that this wise old tree held the answers to life's questions in its lofty branches. These answers were there for those who would climb up high enough in its branches to listen to the wind.

Nane' looked up into the leafy tent to see if there was a possum or raccoon up in the tree, but there was nothing. Tasiki continued looking toward the top of the tree barking loudly. As Eya's dog watched, the brave warrior pulled himself from branch to branch crawling up the huge tree. Below, Tasiki nervously circled the gigantic trunk.

After a climbing a great while, Nane' finally reached the top of the tree. He looked all around. And, out over the treetops, he saw a tiny wisp of smoke, far away to the south. Further, beyond, he saw a huge blue lake. On one side of the lake was beautiful island bathed in sunshine. But the other end was hidden in fog and clouds. Nane' realized he hadn't eaten in days. Maybe where the smoke rose, someone could have food to share. He quickly climbed down the oak and took the southern path towards the blue lake.

Nane' journeyed all night and arrived at the lodge at daybreak. The dwelling had a huge lodge flap door at the front, and appeared so old that the tree bark on its sides was bleached white by years of sunlight. As Nane' approached the lodge he saw a gigantic man appear in the doorway. Tasiki ran ahead to greet the giant. The great man stooped to pat the dog and offer him a piece of meat.

Nane' stopped and stood before the giant. The old man had long white hair with eyes that shone with fiery brilliance from a strong wrinkled face. A long robe of skins was thrown loosely around his shoulders and his hands held a great staff.

Nane' shouted, "Good morning great father. I want to honor you by presenting you with the gift of my knife. We have come a long way and we are looking…"

Suddenly the old chief raised his hand and said, "My name is Meero', great chief of the world, and I know why you have come. Sit down by my fire and have some food. We will talk."

After Nane' had finished eating, he told Meero' of his unhappiness and his determination to follow his love to the Land of Spirits. Meero' replied, "Your lovely maiden passed through my lodge three full moons ago." The great chief took Nane' through the back door of the lodge and pointed toward the lake. Meero' explained, "Do you see that island in the sunlight? That is where Eya is." Then, Meero' pointed to the other end of the lake. Nane' could only see fog and clouds with flashes of lightning within the shrouded mist. Meero' warned, "There lurks danger on that side of the lake. You now stand upon the Land of Spirits' borders, and my lodge is its entrance. No living person has ever entered, but your great courage and love has touched my heart and I will let you travel there alone to visit her for one day. But at sundown, you will see a dark wisp of smoke from my lodge. You must return then. If you need my help call out my name, Meero'." Nane' agreed and rushed toward the lake. When he came to the banks of the broad lake, Nane' saw a white stone canoe tied to a tree. Even though the strange boat was made of shining white stone, it floated like a leaf on the water.

Nane' leaped into the canoe and began paddling toward the beautiful island in the distance. He noticed something strange. Even when Nane' didn't paddle it seemed as if something was pulling his canoe toward the sunlit island. The warm breeze and sound of water was so soothing that Nane' fell into a deep sleep.

When Nane' woke up, he realized that the canoe had been washed far away from the island bathed in sunshine. All Nane' could see was a thick mist surrounding the boat. Lightning bolts sprang from the sky striking the water behind and beside of him, there seemed to be angry voices he could not understand within the thunder. He looked down into the clear water and saw that the bottom of the lake was lined with bones of many people. Boney wrinkled hands reached up through the water and tried to grab his boat, but Nane' used his paddle to push them off. Nane' realized he was getting colder. He tried to paddle and turn himself around, but he could not steer the canoe in the choppy water. Ice began collecting on the sides of the canoe and his paddle. He looked ahead of him and could barely see an island up ahead. As he edged closer, he was able to see twisted leafless trees with long icicles hanging off the bare branches.

At last the canoe stopped and Nane' reached the frozen island. He walked slowly up the bank. Nane' realized the ice and snow was above his ankles and he was very cold. All at once, Nane' heard a moan. In front of him was an old man hunched over digging in the ground with a sharp wooden stick. Nane' spoke up, "Grandfather, what are you doing?" "What am I doing?" sneered the old man. "Don't you know there is nothing here to eat here except for these bitter ground turnips? These dreadful things make my stomach so sour." Now, Nane' was able to see many other people digging in the cold frosty ground. He noticed all the people's bodies were bent over with old age. The toothless man explained, "My name is Senu', when I lived in the Land of the living, I was a great chief among my people. But, I wanted gold, furs, and riches above all else, and when I died, I was sent here." Nane' asked, "Can you tell me how I can get to the other island? I am looking for my lost love, Eya." Senu' grabbed Nane' by the shoulders and whispered in his ear, "Trust me, my son, you would be a fool to try to escape. Moya', who sits on the giant toadstool, acts as a judge to those who enter this island. If you try to escape, Moya' will eat you alive or you will surely die the second death from the lightning within the clouds."

At that moment, Nane' heard a shriek and a hiss. Running through the mist, coming towards them was Moya'. Her face was twisted into a snarl and her head was covered with rattlesnakes instead of hair. Senu' yelled, "Run, run, If she catches you, she will eat you alive. Run!"

Nane' ran back in the direction of the canoe. He could feel Moya's hot breath on the back of his neck. Nane' fell into the water. He quickly pushed the canoe away from the bank, and then he grabbled the side of the boat and pulled himself into the canoe. Moya' stopped at the lakeshore hissing and shrieking.

Lightning struck on all sides of the boat and great waves began to smash the front of the boat. Nane' was aware that there were people struggling through the waves. There were old people and young people.

Just as Nane' thought he would be killed or sank, he grabbed his necklace and shouted, "Please help me!" Meero' heard Nane's call, raised his hand and whispered, "Waro'we!" At that instant the lightning stopped and the waves ceased. Waro'we, the Great Spirit of Life, decided that Nane' should pass safely through for he had led a good life in the land of the Lumbee river.

Nane' had traveled but a few more strokes when he saw something that made his heart leap. Beside him, in another stone canoe, was Eya. He reached his hand towards her, and she smiled but did not speak. Finally, Nane' and Eya' reached the shore of the island bathed in sunshine. Nane' helped Eya' out of her canoe, and with tears in his eyes he held her for a long time without any words.

Together, they wandered over beautiful fields full of flowers. The weather was perfect. There were never any storms, ice, or chilly winds. In this land there was no hunger, war, pain, or death. Nane' and Eya met many people. Each person they met, greeted the couple with a smile. Everyone looked young and appeared to be so happy.

After Nane' and Eya crossed through a deep green forest and strolled through a tall grassy meadow, spread out in front of them was a huge banquet. Nane' and Eya' ate together and laughed the rest of the day. Nane' told Eya' of his love, his journey, the kindness of the chief, Meero', and the terrible island on the other side of the lake. Eya' told Nane' of her love and how happy she felt in her new home.

As sundown approached, Eya' said, "It hurts my heart to see you leave, but it is almost time for you to return." With tears in his eyes Nane' pleaded, "I have searched so far and long for you. I cannot bear to lose you again." Eya' touched Nane's face and said, "Look, the smoke now rises from the great chief's lodge. You must go, for you have come here before your time. You must return to our people to guide them for there are many dark days ahead. Time means nothing to us in the Land of Spirits. I will wait for you until it is your time to return." With a heavy heart, Nane' hugged and kissed Eya' one last time, and climbed back into his canoe. Eya' watched Nane' as he paddled out of sight.

Nane' and Tasiki did return to the Lumbee village. And. Nane' did become chief, and lived out his life as Eya' had foretold. Finally, after Nane' was very old, he went to live in the land of spirits. Today, Nane', Tasiki, and Eya' walk side by side on that sunlit island far away.

THE MOON OF THE TURNING LEAVES
Chicora and the Little People

In modern times, the wise ones say, the "Yeha'suri," or little wild spirit people (also called boogers), left their homes under hollow logs, rotten trees, mounds of mold and fungus, and sink holes deep in the forest to torment children by pinching or poking the young ones with sharp wooden splinters through the cracks in the wooden floors of Lumbee cabins. The Lumbee feared the "Yeha'suri" might also braid the family mule or horses' hair to make mischief.

The annual arrival of the new and old corn also reminded Lumbee families to take clothes inside before evening. It was also a time to remember to use broomsedge brooms to sweep away all their children's footprints before nightfall. These things were done so the Yeha'suri would not create fitful dreams or steal the young one's away during the night. This is an adaptation of a tale shared by Clarence Lowery, Lumbee historian.

Bubble, plop, bubble, plop sings the Lumbee River as it flows slowly past Chicora's village. The Lumbee, people of the river swamp, have lived for hundreds of years beside the dark and mysterious Lumbee river.

One starlit night many years ago, a young girl called Chicora was startled awake by gruff giggling, shuffling, and growling noises coming from outside her family's lodge. She did not move, but opened her eyelids just wide enough to see a pair of tiny hands reach through the lodge flap. She could see the outline of seven or eight childlike shapes in the moonlight. Chicora held onto her shell necklace, chanting silently, "Creator, One who Never Dies, Please protect me."

Finally, Chicora screamed, "Leave me alone.!" At that moment, the little shapes vanished into the night.

All night she lay awake worrying, "Will the little ones come back and try to take me away?"

As the sun lifted one lazy eye over the town, Chicora climbed out of her home at sunrise trembling from the cold. She saw that the spirit of North Wind had painted the trees and earth a snowy white color of the frost. This was the beginning of the short warm time before winter known by her people as "the moon of the turning leaves;" the time of harvest. Chicora looked around the lodge and was surprised to see many footprints in the sand, so much smaller than the tracks made from her moccasins.

Later when the sun stole the day from the night, Eno, the chief of the Lumbee, came out of his lodge. When the village had gathered around, he proclaimed, "Today is the first day of the moon of the turning leaves. Her greatest gift, the corn, is now ripe for harvest. At sunset, we will begin the Corn Dance to honor and celebrate our ancestors and this year's corn harvest."

Quickly, the whole town scattered to get ready for the evening dance. The keeper of the council house fire whispered, "I must put out the old fire which I have tended since the last Corn Dance and find rich pine stump wood to start a new council fire."

The women and children whispered, "We must mend the dancer's torn regalia, gather dried gourds, corn husks, and turtle shell rattles. "Blum, shake, blum, shake, blum," echoed the sounds of the rattles and drums as they sewed bits of bone, shell, and copper into the clothing. The women also thought about how beautiful the dancers would look, shuffling and stomping around the sacred circle.

The men whispered, "We must gather the new pine boughs to replace the old brown branches covering the brush arbor for the drummers, pick up fallen branches, break up dirt clods on the stickball field and chunkey court so we can play games after the dance.

The town was so busy that no one saw a little brown hand pull back the branches of a flame azalea bush near the edge of the village. "Oh no!" snorted a teeny gruff voice coming from behind a flame azalea bush, "Not a Corn Dance, I can just hear them now with their rattles and drums, their whooping, their singing! We must stop it."

While the village scurried around like a busy fire ant mound, Chicora was sitting on a corn grinding log, thinking about what had happened the night before. Chief Eno marched over to Chicora.

"Chicora! Chief Eno said sharply, "I know you like to daydream, but haven't you heard we're having a Corn Dance tonight?"

"Sorry?" asked Chicora, "Could you please say that again?"

Chief Eno sighed, "I want you to please gather some blades and ears of corn for the giving thanks celebration tonight."

"I will, Chief Eno," Chicora yawned. She picked up her pine needle basket and strolled toward the cornfield crunching the autumn leaves as she walked. The whole village called Chicora, "the daydreamer" or "cloudy headed one" because she often seemed lost in thought.

When she finally reached the field, she reached up the tall corn stalk, pulled an ear of corn down, and tore away the husks. She was amazed to see what lay under the silks. She exclaimed, "I have never seen kernel of different colors like this before: sunrise yellow, milkweed white, and sunset red. Our corn has always been the shades the scarlet maple trees turn during the moon of the turning leaves."

As she brushed away more of the silks, she thought she heard a quiet voice warn, "Leave us alone." Chicora let the ear of corn fall to the ground and looked to the left and to the right. She saw nothing. "Perhaps that was just the sound of the wind rustling the corn stalks," she guessed. She took a few slow steps toward the middle of the field and picked another ear and stripped it. This one was the usual red color.

As she was pulling off the silks, a chorus of childlike voices said, **"Leave us alone!"** Chicora froze in her tracks. She thought, "That was not the sound of the wind." Growling and snarling noises came from behind her as she turned around. One of the tiny grim men stepped forward and aimed his short bow at Chicora. Another raised his blowgun and yelled, "Leave Us Alone!!!" Chicora slapped her hand over her mouth, dropped her pinestraw basket, and ran as quickly as the wind back to her family's lodge and dove under a bearskin blanket.

A few moments later, a bright light shone into the small branch covered lodge. "Leave Me Alone," screamed Chicora, pulling the fur blanket more tightly over her head. "Chicora?" asked Chief Eno, kneeling to enter the lodge. "What's wrong?"

Chicora swallowed, cleared her throat, and she told Chief Eno about the snarling little men and the strange corn.

"Ah," smiled Chief Eno. "You have met the Yeha'suri, the little wild spirit people. They must be planning some kind of trick to play on us. We must re-return to the field together." "Hawo," sniffed Chicora, "thank you for believing me."

Half of the sun was shining above the tall trees of the forest when Chicora and Chief Eno walked to the corn-field.

"Tana'ke,," Chief Eno shouted, "I am Eno, chief of the Lumbee. Please leave our cornfield." Chicora was scared, but she though, "I must do something." As a sign of courage, she sang the lulu sound in a high-pitched voice "La, la, la, la, la . . ."

A scream of a wounded swamp cat suddenly rose out of the field. The great cornstalks began to bend and break as if a group of spooked animals were trying to hurry away from them. Chief Eno and Chicora heard them rush out of the field toward the forest.

When Chief Eno entered the cornfield, he bent over to look at the ears of corn Chicora had dropped. To his surprise, one of the ears of corn had kernel of sunrise yellow, milkweed white, and sunset red, while another ear lying near first, was the same strawberry roan (red) color.

Chief Eno understood. He turned around to see Chicora standing behind him quietly. He exclaimed, "Chicora, the Yeha'suri want to make our people afraid (jubious – Ju-bus) to touch this odd-looking corn. The little people were painting the corn and pasting the husks back into place, but they were frightened away before they could finish painting all the ears."

Chief Eno laughed with delight, "Gather more ears of this new corn and take them back to our people. Tell them everything you have seen, and I will be waiting there for you."

Chicora walked toward the people gathered around the sacred circle and proclaimed, "Listen to my story. " She began to tell the tribe about the little men and how they had painted the corn.

When the people saw the ears of colorful corn, the whole town gasped, "What has happened to our corn?" Then some of the townspeople began to murmur, "Isn't this the cloudy-headed one we call the daydreamer? What kind of wild tale has she thought up this time?"

So, she bravely picked up one of the strange ears of corn, walked in front of the crowd at the edge of the sacred circle, took a big bite, "See," she shouted, "It is good." After Chicora took that bite, the Lumbee stopped their whispering, forgot their fear, and let out a great glad cry. Hidden far in the back of the crowd, Chief Eno grinned with pride.

From that day on, Chicora was viewed with respect. Chicora was no longer called "Daydreamer" in the village. Now she was known as "Deep Thinker" because she had shown courage and cleverness when she met the Yeha'suri (the little wild spirit people) in the great field of corn.

And, ever since that time, long ago, the Lumbee have had both the "Big Red" corn and corn in kernel of sunrise yellow, milkweed white, and sunset red.

THE LEGEND OF THE LUMBEE STAR

In 1908, a terrible explosion occurred in Siberia, a wilderness region in central Asia. The shock wave was felt thousands of miles away. The scientists who went to investigate found that the trees for miles around had been blown down like blades of tall grass in a windstorm. They were puzzled because there was no huge hole. The explosion had apparently happened in the air. Scientists guessed that a comet and not a meteor had caused this explosion.

In truth, the Lumbee star portrayed in this tale is not a star at all, but a comet. Astronomers tell us that comets are made of chunks of ice and dust with pockets of gases trapped along with bits of rocky material. That's why some astronomy experts call the comet a "flying dirty snowball."

Astronomers also tell us that when the comet approaches the sun, the ice on the surface of the comet begins to turn into gas. The bits of dust and dirt trail behind the comet into space along with water vapor. These electrically charged particles create a bright streak we see following behind the comet known as "the tail of the comet."

Haley's Comet is perhaps the most famous comet, and it comes into earth's view every seventy five and one-half years. Many people in ancient times viewed the comet's appearance as an evil omen or sign of bad luck.

L ong ago, Chicora and her son Kure' lived in a small lodge, at the edge of a large clearing, near the banks of the dark and mysterious Lumbee river. Kure' and his mother depended on the corn they grew by their beloved river to feed them.

One night while Chicora and her son were sleeping in their pine-branch covered home, Sawana and her twin sons crept near their lodge. Sawana was conjurer and a rootworker. A rootworker is someone who prepares evil potions from plants. Sawana lived with her two sons Ska' and Yeopim near the banks of the Cape Fear river. The twins were bigger and more fierce than two fully grown black bears. After the rootworker and her two sons entered the lodge, Sawana quickly put her hand over Kure's mouth as the twins grabbed his hands and feet and pulled him out of the lodge. After the twins carried the boy outside, Kure' kicked out of the brother's grip, jumped to his feet, and ran as quickly as he could through the meadow towards the forest. The twins caught him before he could reach the woods. Then Yeopim held Kure' up by his throat while Ska' grabbed Kure's hands and tied them behind his back. Kure' tried to yell and warn his mother, but Sawana growled, "If you make another sound we will hurt your mother. Do you understand?" Kure' nodded his head and the twins pushed Chicora's son ahead of them into the darkness. Sawana sneered, "I'm going back to look in on your mother and she had better be asleep." Chicora was sleeping so deeply she did not hear anything. Sawana smiled, closed the lodge flap, and ran to catch up to Kure' and her sons.

The next morning Chicora awoke at sunrise. She was surprised Kure' was not in their lodge so she lifted up the flap and called outside, "Kure', where are you?" There was no answer. Chicora went to the bank of the brooding and mysterious Lumbee river and shouted, "Kure', Are you fishing?" Still no answer. Kure's mother worriedly rubbed her face as she waded through the tall green stalks of the cornfield yelling, "Son, are you playing a hide and seek game with me?" Again no answer. She cried, "Kure, Where are you?" No answer. Chicora collapsed in despair and began to sob loudly fearing that her son was lost or dead.

As Chicora was sobbing, she heard a call that sounded like, "koot, **koot**, **koot**, koot, koot, rah" Chicora looked up through her tears and saw Kootsin the pileated woodpecker. Kootsin looked down on Chicora from high in a longleaf pine tree and asked, "Oo-rah, what is wrong?" Chicora replied, "My son is missing and I can't find him anywhere." Kootsin replied, "I think I can find Kure' but you will need to give me something first." Chicora cried, "Bird, I don't have anything I can give you. This lodge, the corn in the field, and a few other small things are all I own." Then Kootsin cooed, "I can find him if you will give me one of your shiny copper earrings and a cake of cornbread."

Chicora asked the woodpecker to wait while she went to her lodge to make some cakes of cornbread from some fresh ground meal. Then Chicora wiped her eyes and laid one of her shiny copper earrings, the last gift her husband had given her, on a large wooden plate beside one cake of cornbread. The she carried the plate, the cornbread, and the earring to the edge of the cornfield, and stepped backwards towards the forest. The woodpecker flew down, gobbled up the cornbread, and carefully scooped the earring up in his beak. As Kootsin flew off across the Lumbee River he called, "Bare'! Bare', (good) I will search to find your son.

Chicora laid her broomstraw mat under the Longleaf Pinetree where she had first saw Kootsin. After four days, Chicora had given up all hope that Kootsin was coming back. She began rolling up her mat and prepared to go look for her son. Chicora wondered, "Did Kootsin lie to me or could he not find Kure'?" At that moment, she heard a faint call coming from up the river. "Rah, Oorah." Chicora was blinded by the late evening sun, but when she peered up into the sky, she thought she could see something flying towards her. Before she could shout "Tana'ke (hello)," the woodpecker was circling overhead crying, "Cape Fear, Cape Fear! Hurry, hurry! Behind Raven Rock! Bring food and a long rope!

Danger! Cape Fear, Cape Fear!" She yelled, "Kootsin Wo'nai're (Bird thank you)" because she knew where she could find her son.

Chicora grabbed her twisted walking cane. Then she packed a long rope and put four cakes of cornbread in a huge deerskin pack and began her journey the same evening. She traveled for many days and nights. When she felt so weak she did not think her legs would carry her another step, she looked up to see the Raven Rock and knew she had finally arrived at the great Cape Fear River.

Chicora felt a small burst of energy as she walked up river and found what looked like stepping stones made of flat, rough, creamy-brown, rocks. She hopped slowly from one to the next to reach the other side of the wide river. After she had crossed the river, Chicora looked up and in front of her loomed Raven Rock. She crawled around the rock, and on the other side of the cliff, she saw one large lodge with three smaller lodges set in a small grassy clearing. The large lodge was made with red mud walls with a broomstraw roof covering the top. The smaller lodges were made of bent saplings and branches and covered with tree bark. Chicora saw signs that people had been there not long ago because there were smoldering ashes in front of the largest lodge. Old bones, broken bowls, and corn husks were scattered everywhere on the ground.

Chicora's feet were cut and badly bruised from the long journey, but she was able to limp slowly up to the big lodge and call out "Kure', are you there?" She heard a faint "Himba (yes)" coming from the forest. Chicora followed the voice and found her son tied up to a big Elm tree at the edge of the woods. As Chicora was untying her son, he told her "Mother, I knew you would come. I was worried that I would never see you again.

We can't talk long because Sawana and the twins left just not long after dawn to go hunting and I expect them back soon." After Chicora untied Kure', he reached behind him a pulled out a copper earring and explained, "The woodpecker came to visit me and gave me your earring to let me know that Sawana had not harmed you. Kootsin told me he would fly back as fast as his wings would carry him to tell you where you could find me.

Chicora gave her son the last cake of cornbread she had. He hungrily ate it and exclaimed, "Mother, this is the best cornbread I have ever tasted." Kure' had not eaten in days because Sawana had barely enough food for herself and her two sons.

After Kure' finished the cornbread, Chicora and Kure' heard, crack, crunch, crunch, crunch, coming up the path. It was Sawana, Ska', and Yeopim coming back to their lodges after the hunt. Chicora took the rope out of the pack and hid in a huge hollow log beside of the big Elm tree. Kure' sat down in front of the huge trunk and put his hands through the ropes so Sawana and her sons would believe he was still tied up.

Sawana was the first to come up the path. Sawana sneered at Kure'. The twin's mother then walked over and picked up the deerskin pack, sat down on the hollow long, and asked her sons, "Which one of you left this fine pack outside?" Yeopim and Ska' looked at each otherand shrugged their shoulders . Sawana growled, "It doesn't matter. We can use it to pack up the meatfrom the deer we just killed." Sawana then dropped the pack, looked at her sons and whined, "I'm getting hungry and sleepy. Come into my lodge and we'll eat some leftover cornmush and take a nap." Sawana rose to her feet, looked over her shoulder at Kure' and mumbled, "You poor little boy! You will have to go hungry again because there is only enough food for my sons and me to eat."

After they crawled into their lodges, Kure' whispered to his mother, "Mother are you alright? Did Sawana crush you when she sat on top of the log? "No," chuckled Chicora from inside the log. Chicora squirmed out of log and said, "You had better leave without me. Sawana and the twins will have no trouble catching me. I am still very weak and lame from my long journey." Kure' knew it was true. Sawana and the twins could catch up to them quickly. Kure' thought for a moment, looked around, and put the deerskin pack in his lap. Then, with a sharp stone, he cut the pack straps in a number of places so it would break when the twins or their mother tried to carry the heavy load of venison. Kure' put the pack in the same place that Sawana had dropped it. Chicora began to wiggle back into the log to wait for Sawana and her sons.

Later that evening, after Sawana and her sons finally came out of the lodge, Sawana turned and looked at Kure' and sneered, "I will hunt you down if you try to escape, and if we can't find you, we will hurt your mother." The Yeopim scowled at Kure' as he picked up the deerskin pack. The three of them disappeared in the forest walking toward the riverbank.

It was near sunset when the twins and their mother found the deer they had killed. The twins immediately began to clear away the dirt and leaves they had used to hide the deer, and Ska' took out his knife and Yeopim helped put in all the venison that the pack could hold. After the twins had packed the bulging sack, Yeopim slung the pack across his shoulder and Ska' exclaimed, "Apo, apo, Tamhyu (Oh, No!) for he saw the pack had broken and the entire load of venison had fallen out onto the ground.

Sawana shrieked, "We need this meat to survive. Hurry! and don't leave anything." She looked closely at the pack and saw that it had been cut. She screamed, "That little slug somehow cut the straps of the pack. Hurry let's get back the camp!"

The sun was now disappearing below the horizon, and the sky filled with dark clouds. As a hard rain began to fall, the water of the Cape Fear began to churn and froth. Kure' knew that his mother was too weak to hop over the stones without the aid of a rope. He crossed the river on the stones and tied the end of the long rope around a big yellow pine tree on the opposite bank.

The rocks were now slippery and the water was splashing around Kure's ankles as he came back to the bank where his mother was waiting. Chicora and Kure' saw a brilliant flash of lightning and heard a loud boom of thunder as they peered up at Raven Rock. Sawana stood on top of the rock shouting, "You may run and hide but you cannot escape. We will find you. I swear we will hunt you both down."

After Sawana yelled these words, Kure' grabbed the thick twine and stood behind his mother shouting, "Mother hold on tight to my arm and the rope." It was nighttime now as Chicora and Kure' began to stumble across the river by holding on tightly to the rope and feeling for the slick stones with their feet. The cold swift water was now knee high and splashing up around their waists. They stumbled and fell many times even though they stepped very slowly, for the stepping stones were deep underwater and the current was very strong.

Kure' and Chicora finally reached the other side of the river. Chicora fell down in the sand weeping, "I am so tired. I cannot go another step. Son, I love you, but you will have to go on without me." Kure' pleaded, "We have to go **NOW!** Look! Sawana and her sons are almost here. They are holding onto our rope and following us across the river on the stones!" But Chicora was too weary to rise to her feet. Kure' cried, "No, I'm not leaving here without you." Kure saw that he twins and their mother were already half way across the river. Sawana, Ska', and Yeopim had wrapped the twine around their wrists so they would not fall down into the black swirling water.

They were coming swiftly across the river. Kure' looked at the twins, their mother, and then peered at the tied rope. With rain splashing in his eyes, Kure' grabbed the beads around his neck and pleaded, "My father, whose voice in the wind I hear, listen to your child. I know you did not bring my mother and I back together only to separate us again. Please protect us." Sawana jeered, "Pray, little boy, beg all you want. It will not do you any good!"

At that moment, the rain stopped as quickly as it had began and the clouds gave way to twinkling stars. One of the stars began to fall from the sky with a loud hiss and a sound like thunder. It stopped just above the waters of the Cape Fear. Then, the gleaming starlike object began to make a loud rumble as it moved slowly up the river shining brightly above the water. Chicora had seen falling stars before but had never seen one so up closely. The streaming ball was gliding just a little higher than the yellow pine trees that lined the bank of the Cape Fear. It was pearly white in color and was covered looked to be giant triangle shaped rocks. The strange object was wider than half the width of the river, and the force of the streaming ball made a deep u-shaped trench in the water. Sawana, Ska', Yeopim, Kure, and Chicora stared in wide-eyed wonder at the glowing spiked object coming towards them from down river.

Suddenly, Kure' thought, "If I could only snag one of those jagged rocks with this water logged rope, it could be the answer to my prayer." Kure' ran to the yellow pine tree and loosed the coil around it. The rope immediately went slack causing the twins and their mother to fall backwards into the river. Growling and gritting their teeth, Sawana and the twins found their footing and began taking long strides, drawing closer. Kure' then grabbed the untied end of the rope out of the water and with cold shaking hands, he tried to fashion a large loop in the end of the long strand. Kure' had tied a loop many times to use in animal traps, but he had never had to tie one so quickly with cold wet hands.

The star was now passing directly in front of Kure' and Chicora. Sawana and her sons were within a few feet of the bank. Kure' knew he had just one chance to save himself and his mother. With all the hope, faith, and strength he could find, Kure' threw the rope. The coiled loop snagged one of the jagged extensions on the side of the gleaming ball.

Kure' and his mother watched in wonder as the star suddenly gained speed and lifted into the sky. Sawana, Yeopim, and Ska's eyes became wide with fear and they began to scream, "You tricked us! Let us go!" They were not able to become loose of the rope now looped around their wrists and wrapped around their legs. The long strand pulled Sawana, Ska', and Yeopim down the river then up into the air. Chicora and Kure' watched as the twins and their mother vanished into the night sky yelling, "**LET US GO! LET US GO! LET US GO!** LET US GO! LET US GO!": Sawana, Ska' and Yeopim had become "the tail of the comet."

After Sawana and the twins disappeared into the night sky. Kure' knelt down in the sand with his mother, on the bank of the river, and they both gave thanks to their heavenly father, Waro'we (God), for his miracle.

Chicora and Kure' rested that night on the bank of the Cape Fear River, then they traveled slowly back to their haven of rest along the Lumbee river. The old ones say that Kootsin, Chicora, and Kure' lived there on the banks of their beloved dark river in peace and happiness for many years.

Vernon Cooper, Lumbee wisdomkeeper, revered elder, and herbal remedy/lore specialist stated that his earliest memories involved a far away train whistle, a long tailed comet, and helping his mother cut strips of cloth (triangles) to make a design in each quilt. He states we would cut so many strips for each design. His mother called each design a star.

In honor of the strong love that the Lumbee hold for their heavenly father and each other, Lumbee ladies still proudly sew the "Lumbee Star" or "Pinecone Patchwork" design in to their quilts, shawls, and to the front of their aprons and dresses. Hayes Alan Locklear, Alvina Blanks and Kat Littleturtle ingeniously incorporated this into shawls, and other regalia Lumbee princesses and lady dancers wear on special occasions. The "Lumbee Star" features some/all of these colors-red, green, blue, white indigo, and pink. Red is displayed because it is the color of sacrifice and the pileated woodpecker's top head feathers. The color green is also placed in the "Lumbee star" because green is the color of the cornstalks in summer and the color of the pinetree which the Lumbee have used for their shelter, medicine, baskets, warmth, and livelihood for centuries. Finally, white is sometimes placed within the star to show purity and the inner strength we receive when we place our faith in God and each other. Sometimes pink and indigo with small white flecks is used to show honor to the wondrous night/evening sky with twinkling stars from which God sent the "Lumbee Star." Epta Tewa Newa'sin (Creator, We Love You).

Symbolism of the Eagle Feather

A Lumbee Story, shared by
Sharon Locklear, publisher of Metrolina Pow Wow

In the beginning, God gave to the animals and birds wisdom, knowledge, and the power to talk to men. The animals and the little wild spirit people would teach a chosen man sacred songs and dance, as well as, much ritual and lore.

The creature most loved by God was the eagle, for this great bird tells the story of life. The Eagle has only two eggs, and all living things in the world are divided into two. There is man and woman or male and female. This is also true with animals, birds, trees, and flowers. All things have children of two kinds so that life may continue. Man has two eyes, two hands, two feet and he has a body and soul or substance and shadow.

Through his eyes, he sees pleasant and unpleasant scenes. Through his nostrils, he smells good and bad odors. With his ears, he hears joyful news and words that make him sad. His mind is divided between good and evil. His right hand may often be used for evil, such as making war or striking a person in anger. But his left hand, which is near his heart, is often full of kindness. His right foot may lead him in down the wrong path, but his left foot could lead him in the right direction.

And so it goes, within him, he has daylight and darkness, summer and winter, war and peace, and life and death.

In order to remember this lesson of life, look to the great eagle, the favorite bird of God. The eagle feather itself if also divided into two parts, part light and part dark. Like man, this feather represents daylight and darkness or summer and winter. For the white tells of summer, when all is bright and cheerful. The black represents the cold dark days of winter.

My children, remember what I tell you. For it is YOU who will choose the path in life you will follow.

Doth the eagle mount up at thy command, and make her nest on high? (Job 39:27 KJV)

About the Author

Arvis Boughman is an enrolled member of the Lumbee Indian tribe of North Carolina. He has worked with adults and children, from many different cultures including Native American children from the Lumbee, Eastern Band of Cherokee, and Sioux tribes.

In 2003 he coauthored *Herbal Remedies of the Lumbee Indians* with Loretta Oxendine. In 2010, he authored *Chicora and the Little People, The Legend of the Indian Corn.* This was the first children's picture book based on the Lumbee Indian culture.

Arvis' hobbies include reading the Bible, fishing, woodcarving, riding horses, gardening, studying Native American cultures and folklore, doing family activities, attending powwows, and listening to old-time and blue-grass music.

Lightning Source UK Ltd.
Milton Keynes UK
UKHW012221261020
372256UK00001B/281